Learn Python
through Nursery Rhymes and Fairy Tales

By Shari Eskenas

Illustrated by Ana Quintero Villafraz

SUNDAE ELECTRONICS

Enjoy learning the Python® programming language!
"Python" is a registered trademark of the Python Software Foundation

Published by Sundae Electronics LLC
https://www.sundaelectronics.com

First edition 2022.
Printed in the United States of America

ISBN 978-1-7359079-6-3 (Hardcover)
ISBN 978-1-7359079-8-7 (Paperback)
ISBN 978-1-7359079-7-0 (eBook)

Table of Contents

NURSERY RHYMES

FAIRY TALES

Dear Apprentice,

I'm so glad you've arrived at Python Castle! A magical experience awaits you- you'll see computer code transformed into classic nursery rhymes and fairy tales!

Once upon a time in a faraway land, there was an enchanted computer deep in the woods. The computer told nursery rhymes and fairy tales using **code**, which is a set of instructions written for a computer to perform tasks, such as printing text to the screen or playing a video.

A **program** is a collection of code that can be run by a computer. The enchanted computer told the nursery rhymes and fairy tales using programs written in the **Python programming language**. Every programming language has its own set of rules for how the code is written, which is called the syntax. Different programming languages are written with different **syntax** and designed for different uses.

People from the nearby village occasionally wandered into the forest and listened to the enchanted computer's stories. Over the years, the Python programs stored on the computer were written down and recorded in a book. You will now be presented with these Python programs. **Your journey has just begun!** There are instructions at the end of this book for running the enchanted programs on **YOUR** computer!

Warm Regards,
S.E.

Row, Row, Row Your Boat

Row, row, row your boat
Gently down the stream
Merrily merrily, merrily, merrily
Life is but a dream

```
# Row Your Boat

print("Row, row, row your boat")
print("Gently down the stream")
print("Merrily merrily, merrily, merrily")
print("Life is but a dream")
```

Lines of code can be separated with empty lines just to make the code easier to read.

`# Row Your Boat` is called a **comment**, which is indicated by the hash symbol (#) in front of the line. It is written as a note for someone reading the code and is ignored by the computer. A comment can explain the purpose of the code or how it works.

A **statement** is a complete program instruction that is run (executed) by a computer to perform an action. A program's statements are executed from top to bottom. The first statement in this program is `print("Row, row, row your boat")`, which prints Row, row, row your boat on the screen.

`print()` is a **function** that is built into the Python language. A function is a block of code that contains instructions to perform a specific task. The code block is run (executed) when the function is called with its name followed by parentheses. The `print()` function prints the string passed to it within the parentheses to the standard output device (computer screen). A string is a sequence of characters (letters, numbers, symbols, or spaces). A string can be written within two single (') or two double (") quotation marks.

The string `"Row, row, row your boat"` is passed to the `print()` function. The `print()` function adds a **newline** character to the end of the string, so the next `print()` function's text will be printed on the next line.

When the program is executed, the four `print()` functions print the following text on the screen:
```
Row, row, row your boat
Gently down the stream
Merrily merrily, merrily, merrily
Life is but a dream
```

Star Light, Star Bright

Star light, star bright,
First star *I* see tonight;
I wish *I* may, *I* wish *I* might,
Have the wish *I* wish tonight.

```
# Make a wish on a star

star_light_level = "bright"
star_order = "First"
print("Star light, star " + star_light_level + ",")
print(star_order  + " star I see tonight;")
print("I wish I may, I wish I might,")
print("Have the wish I wish tonight.")
```

`star_light_level` is called a **variable**, which stores a value. A variable is given a name and created once a value is assigned to it. It can be given any name- `star_light_level` was chosen because it's a meaningful name. You assign a value to a variable with an equal sign (=), which is called an **assignment operator**. The value on the right side of the equal sign is assigned to the variable on the left side of the equal sign. **Operators** are special symbols that perform operations on values or variables. In this program, the string `"bright"` is the value assigned to the `star_light_level` variable and the string `"First"` is assigned to the `star_order` variable.

Variable names are conventionally written in lowercase letters and an underscore (_) separates words in the name because variable names cannot contain blank spaces. They can contain letters, numbers, and underscores. A variable name cannot start with a number.

Concatenation is the process of combining multiple strings together. In this program, the plus sign (+) operator is used to concatenate (combine) strings. In the first `print()` function, the string `"bright"` stored in `star_light_level` is concatenated with the strings `"Star light, star "` and `","`. There is an empty space before the end quotation marks in `"Star light, star "`, which creates a space between `star` and `bright` in the new string.

The next `print()` function concatenates the string `"First"` stored in `star_order` with `" star I see tonight;"`.

The four `print()` functions print these lines:
```
Star light, star bright,
First star I see tonight;
I wish I may, I wish I might,
Have the wish I wish tonight.
```

Hickory Dickory Dock

Hickory, dickory, dock.
The mouse ran up the clock.
The clock struck one,
The mouse ran down,
Hickory, dickory, dock.

```python
first = "Hickory"
middle = "dickory"
last = "dock"

print(first + ", " + middle + ", " + last)
mouse_run_direction = "up"
print("The mouse ran " + mouse_run_direction + " the clock.")
clock_hour = 1
print("The clock struck " + str(clock_hour) + ",")
mouse_run_direction = "down"
print("The mouse ran " + mouse_run_direction + ",")
print(first + ", " + middle + ", " + last)
```

A variable can be re-assigned a new value. The value of the variable `mouse_run_direction` is first assigned as "up" and printed in a sentence. The variable's value is re-assigned to be "down" before being printed again in a sentence.

The variable `clock_hour` is assigned a value of 1, which is an integer (a whole number without a decimal point). Since 1 is not enclosed within quotation marks, `clock_hour` has an **integer data type**. A value's data type determines how it can be used. For example, a string can be concatenated with another string, but a string cannot be concatenated with an integer.

Python's built-in function `str()` converts the data type of the value within parentheses into a string data type. In this program, the `clock_hour` value of 1 must be converted from an integer into a string so it can be concatenated with other strings in `print()`.

The five `print()` functions print the following lines to the screen:
```
Hickory, dickory, dock
The mouse ran up the clock.
The clock struck 1,
The mouse ran down,
Hickory, dickory, dock
```

Rain, Rain, Go Away

Rain, rain, go away
Come again another day
Little Johnny wants to play.

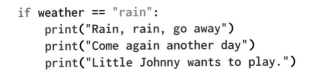

```python
weather = "rain"

if weather == "rain":
    print("Rain, rain, go away")
    print("Come again another day")
    print("Little Johnny wants to play.")
```

An `if` statement is a conditional statement that tests if a condition is true or false. It begins with the `if` keyword. Keywords are reserved words that have special meanings in Python, so they cannot be used as variable or function names.

An **expression** is a piece of code that evaluates to a single value. The expression on the first line of the `if` statement, which must end with a colon (:), is the condition that is tested for being true or false.

If the `if` statement's condition is true, its **code block** is executed. A code block is indicated by indented lines, which must all be at the same level of indentation. Conventionally, lines in a code block are indented by four spaces, but they can be indented by any number of spaces if they're all indented by the same amount. In this program, the code block consists of three lines.

In the `if` statement's condition (conditional expression), `weather == "rain"`, the double equal sign (==) is called an **equality operator**. This is a type of comparison (relational) operator, which compares the relation between two values. The equality operator tests if the value on the left side of the operator is equal to the value on the right side of the operator.

Since `weather` was assigned a value of `"rain"`, the expression `weather == "rain"` is true, so the `if` statement's condition is true and its code block is executed. The `print()` functions print these lines:
```
Rain, rain, go away
Come again another day
Little Johnny wants to play.
```

Humpty Dumpty

Humpty Dumpty sat on a wall,
Humpty Dumpty had a great fall.
All the king's horses and all the king's men
Couldn't put Humpty together again.

```python
humpty_dumpty_together = True
humpty_on_wall = True
accident = None

if humpty_on_wall:
    print("Humpty Dumpty sat on a wall,")
    accident = "a great fall"

if accident == "a great fall":
    print("Humpty Dumpty had a great fall.")
    humpty_dumpty_together = False

if not humpty_dumpty_together:
    print("All the king's horses and all the king's men")
    print("Couldn't put Humpty together again.")
```

Python's **Boolean** data type (also called the **bool** data type) consists of only two values: True and False. True and False are Python keywords that must have their first letters capitalized and the rest of the letters in lowercase. When an expression is tested for being true or false, the result will have a Boolean data type. The keyword None indicates there is no value and evaluates to False. In this program, None is assigned to **accident**.

After an if statement's condition is tested, it is evaluated to be a Boolean value of True or False. The first if statement's header could also be written as if humpty_on_wall == True, but this is redundant because any if condition evaluates to a Boolean value and does not need to be directly compared to True. Since
humpty_on_wall stores the value of True, the if condition evaluates to True and the code block is executed. In the code block, the value of **accident** is set to be "a great fall".

The second if statement is executed because **accident** stores the value of "a great fall". In the code block, humpty_dumpty_together is assigned the value of False.

The not keyword is a **logical operator** that inverts an expression's Boolean value. This is called the logical NOT operation. If the expression after not is true, the operator returns False. If the expression after not is false, the operator returns True.

Since humpty_dumpty_together stores False, the expression not humpty_dumpty_together evaluates to True and the third if statement is executed.

Jack and Jill

Jack and Jill went up the hill
To fetch a pail of water.
Jack fell down and broke his crown,
And Jill came tumbling after.

```python
jack_direction = "up"
jill_direction = "up"
purpose = "fetch a pail of water"
if jack_direction == "up" and jill_direction == "up":
    print("Jack and Jill went up the hill to " + purpose)
    jack_fall = True
    if jack_fall:
        print("Jack fell down")
        jack_crown_broke = True
        jill_fall = True
    else:
        print("Mission accomplished.")
        jack_crown_broke = False
        jill_fall = False

    if jack_crown_broke:
        print("and broke his crown")

    if jill_fall:
        print("and Jill came tumbling after")
```

The keyword and is a logical operator that combines two conditions by testing if both conditions are true. If both conditions to the right and left side of the and operator are true, the overall expression is evaluated to be True. Otherwise, the overall expression is evaluated to be False. Since jack_direction stores a value of "up" and jill_direction stores a value of "up", the expression jack_direction == "up" and jill_direction == "up" evaluates to True and the if code block is executed.

An inner (nested) if…else statement is within the code block of the outer if statement. If the if statement's condition is true, its code block is executed. If the if statement's condition is false, the else code block is executed instead. Since the value of jack_fall is True, the first inner if code block is executed. After Jack fell down is printed, the values of jack_crown_broke and jill_fall are both set to True. Therefore, the following two nested if statements are executed. This prints and broke his crown followed by and Jill came tumbling after on the next line.

Peter Piper

Peter Piper picked a peck of pickled peppers.
If Peter Piper picked a peck of pickled peppers,
Where's the peck of pickled peppers Peter Piper picked?

```python
jars = ["chocolates", "fruit candies", "pickled peppers", "gummy bears"]

item_picked = jars[2] #save "pickled peppers" in item_picked

jars.remove("pickled peppers")

print("Peter Piper picked a peck of " + item_picked)

if item_picked == "pickled peppers":
    print("Where's the peck of pickled peppers Peter Piper picked?")
    print("\nI only see these jars now:")
    print(jars)
```

jars is a variable that holds a **list**, which is a Python data type. It stores an ordered sequence of items (also called elements) that are separated by commas between two brackets ([ ]). A list can contain items of any data type and the items can be of different data types. The list jars initially contains these strings: "chocolates", "fruit candies", "pickled peppers", and "gummy bears".

Each item in a list can be accessed with its index number within brackets. The first item in a list starts at an index (position number) of 0. The list's first item is stored in jars[0] and the list's second item is stored in jars[1]. item_picked is assigned the list's third item, jars[2], which is "pickled peppers".

A **method** is a function that can perform an action on data. remove() is a built-in Python method that removes a specified item from a list. In this program, the remove() method removes the item "pickled peppers" from the jars list. The remove() method is called (executed) using **dot notation**. A dot (.) is required between the variable name jars and the method name remove. The item "pickled peppers" within the remove() parentheses is passed to the method.

Since "pickled peppers" was stored in item_picked before being removed from the list, Peter Piper picked a peck of pickled peppers is then printed. At the end of the if statement that is executed, the jars list is printed, which no longer contains the item "pickled peppers". In the second print() in the if statement, the \n is a **newline character** that adds an empty line before the string I only see these jars now: is printed.

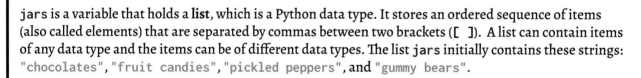

Candy Shop

Peppers

Hey Diddle Diddle

Hey diddle, diddle!
The cat and the fiddle,
The cow jumped over the moon;
The little dog laughed
To see such sport,
And the dish ran away with the spoon.

```python
name = "diddle"
print("Hey " + name + ", " + name + "!")

things = ["cat","fiddle","spoon","moon","cow","little dog","dish"]

print("The " + things[0] + " and the " + things[1])
print("The " + things[4] + " jumped over the " + things[3])
print("The " + things[5] + " laughed\nTo see such sport,")

thing_leaving = things.pop(6)
thing_taken = things.pop(2)

print("And the " + thing_leaving + " ran away with the " + thing_taken)

print("\nThings left:")
for thing in things:
    print(thing)
```

After the first print() prints Hey diddle, diddle!, the following three print() functions print the items of the things list in these sentences:
```
The cat and the fiddle
The cow jumped over the moon
The little dog laughed
To see such sport,
```

The newline character (\n) between laughed and To in print() creates a new line so the text To see such sport, is printed on the next line after The little dog laughed.

Python's built-in pop() method removes an item from a list and allows you to access the item's value after it's removed. By default, pop() removes the last item in a list, but you can remove any item by including its index in parentheses. things.pop(6) removes the seventh item (because the index of the first list item starts at 0). The removed item "dish" is returned by pop() and stored in thing_leaving. The next removed item is "spoon", which is stored in thing_taken.

A for loop can be used to loop (iterate) over the items in a list and perform an action with each item. In this program, the for loop repeats for each item in the things list. There must be a colon at the end of the first line. For each loop iteration, the current list item is stored in the loop variable thing and the for code block is executed. The loop variable can have any name, but it's good practice to give it a meaningful name. In the for code block, the current list item stored in thing is printed on its own line.

Little Bo-Peep

Little Bo-Peep has lost her sheep,
and doesn't know where to find them;
leave them alone, and they'll come home,
bringing their tails behind them.

```python
sheep_at_home = ["sheep #1", "sheep #2", "sheep #3", "sheep #4", "sheep #5"]

if sheep_at_home:
    num_sheep = len(sheep_at_home)
    print("There are " + str(num_sheep) + " sheep at home\n")

del sheep_at_home[2:4]  # Delete sheep #3 and sheep #4
num_sheep = len(sheep_at_home)
print("Now there are " + str(num_sheep) + " sheep at home:")
for sheep in sheep_at_home:
    print(sheep)

del sheep_at_home[:]  # Deletes whole list
rhyme = """Little Bo-Peep has lost her sheep,
and doesn't know where to find them;
leave them alone, and they'll come home,
bringing their tails behind them."""
if not sheep_at_home:
    print("\nAll the sheep left the house!\n")
    print(rhyme)
```

A non-empty list evaluates to True and an empty list evaluates to False. Since sheep_at_home is a non-empty list, the first if statement is executed. The built-in Python function len() returns the length (number of items) of the sheep_at_home list. The length of 5 is stored in num_sheep, which is converted into a string with str() in print(). There are 5 sheep at home is printed.

A **slice** allows you to access part of a list with a starting and ending index. sheep_at_home[2:4] creates a slice containing items with indexes of 2 and 3 ("sheep #3" and "sheep #4") because the ending index (4) is not included. The del keyword deletes the list slice sheep_at_home[2:4] without giving access to it after it has been removed from the list. The del keyword can also be used to remove a single list item. Now there are 3 sheep at home: is printed and the for loop prints the items of the list, which are now "sheep #1", "sheep #2", and "sheep #5".

If you omit the starting index of a slice, it begins at the list's first item. If you omit the ending index, the slice ends through the last item. The slice sheep_at_home[:] includes the whole list, which is deleted with del. sheep_at_home is now empty, and an empty list evaluates to False. Therefore, the expression not sheep_at home evaluates to True and the last if statement is executed.

As an alternative to creating a multi-line string using newline (\n) characters, you can use **triple quotes** (with either double quotes or single quotes) on each side of the string. In this program, rhyme is assigned a multi-line string. In the assignment, the last three lines are not indented, which makes them align with the first line when rhyme is printed.

The Muffin Man

Do you know the muffin man?
The muffin man, the muffin man.
Do you know the muffin man
Who lives in Drury Lane?

```python
person_info = {"name": "the muffin man", "street address": "Drury Lane"}
print("Do you know " + person_info["name"] + "?")
print(person_info["name"] + ", " + person_info["name"] + ".")
print("Do you know " + person_info["name"])
print("Who lives in " + person_info["street address"] + "?")
```

person_info is a **dictionary**, which is a Python data type. It is a collection of items that store related pieces of information within curly braces ({}). Each item in a dictionary consists of a **key** and its associated **value**, which are separated by a colon (:) and called a **key : value pair**. The dictionary's items are separated by commas. A dictionary's values can be of any data type. A dictionary's keys must be of a data type such as an integer or string that is **immutable**, which means the values of the keys can't change. An example of a **mutable** data type is a list because the items it contains can be updated.

In the person_info dictionary, the key "name" has a value of "the muffin man" and the key "street address" has a value of "Drury Lane".

A key's value is accessed by including the key in brackets ([ ]) after the dictionary's name. To access the value of the "name" key, use person_info["name"]. To access the value of the "street address" key, use person_info["street address"]. The print() functions print these lines using the person_info dictionary values:

```
Do you know the muffin man?
the muffin man, the muffin man.
Do you know the muffin man
Who lives in Drury Lane?
```

This Little Piggy

This little piggy went to market,
This little piggy stayed home,
This little piggy had roast beef,
This little piggy had none.
This little piggy went...
Wee, wee, wee,
all the way home!

```python
piggy_activities = {
    "Piggy #1": "went to market",
    "Piggy #2": "stayed home",
    "Piggy #3": "had roast beef",
    "Piggy #4": None,
    "Piggy #5": "went wee, wee, wee, all the way home!"
    }

for piggy, activity in piggy_activities.items():
    if piggy == "Piggy #4":
        print("Piggy #4 had " + str(activity))
    else:
        print(piggy + " " + activity)
```

To define a dictionary over multiple lines, it's good practice to format it like the `piggy_activities` dictionary. Python's built-in `items()` method returns a list containing the key:value pairs in a dictionary. The `for` loop uses `items()` to loop through the key:value pairs in the `piggy_activities` dictionary.

Two variables (`piggy` and `activity` in this program) are used to store each key and value. Any name can be chosen for the variables that hold each key and value. In each iteration of the `for` loop, the variable `piggy` stores the key of the current key:value pair and the variable `activity` stores the value of the current key:value pair. In the first iteration of the `for` loop, piggy stores `"Piggy #1"` and activity stores `"went to market"`. The `else` code block is executed and `Piggy #1 went to market` is printed.

`"Piggy #4"` has a value of `None`, which needs to be converted into a string with `str()` to be concatenated with a string in `print()`. Also, the word "had" needs to be added to the sentence. Therefore, an `if` statement is used to execute a different `print()` function for the key `"Piggy #4"` than the other keys.

Important note: In earlier versions of Python (below version 3.7), dictionaries were **unordered**, which meant that the order of key:value pairs was not preserved and the `items()` method returned the key:value pairs in an unpredictable order. Therefore, if you're using Python version 3.6 or below, you probably won't see each key:value pair printed in order. Dictionaries are **ordered** in Python version 3.7 and above.

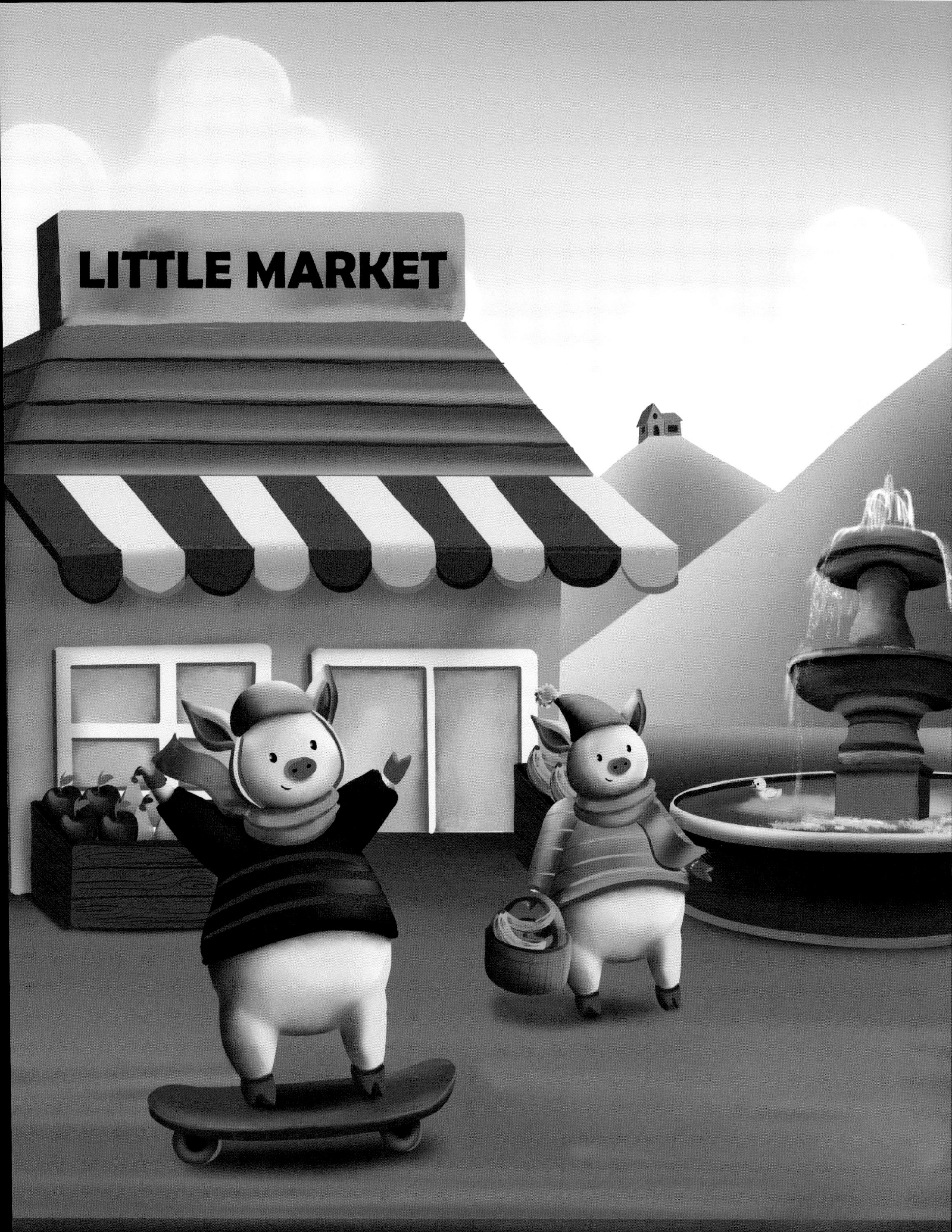
LITTLE MARKET

One Potato, Two Potatoes

One potato, two potatoes,
Three potatoes, four!
Five potatoes, six potatoes,
Seven potatoes, more!

```python
potatoes = 0

for potato_count in range(1,8):
        potatoes = potatoes + 1
        if potato_count == 1:
                print("One potato")
        elif potato_count == 4:
                print("Four!")
        else:
                print(str(potatoes) + " potatoes,")

print("more!")
```

A `for` loop can be used to loop (iterate) over its code block for a specified number of times using `range()`. The built-in Python function `range()` generates a sequence of integer numbers. In this program, the range start value is 1 and the stop value is 8, which creates integer values from 1 through 7 because the stop value is not included.

The `for` loop repeats for each integer value from 1 through 7 that is created from the `range()` function. Therefore, the `for` loop repeats seven times. For each iteration of the loop, the current number generated by `range()` is stored in the variable `potato_count`.

The statement `potatoes = potatoes + 1` assigns the value of `potatoes + 1` to `potatoes`, which increases the `potatoes` value by 1 using the **addition operator** (+). Since the `potatoes` value increases by 1 during each loop, it follows the value of `potato_count`.

You can add any number of test conditions to an `if…else` statement with `elif`, which is short for "else if". If there are multiple true conditions, only the code block of the first true condition is executed. If the `potato_count` value is 1, the `if` code block is executed, which prints `One potato`. If the `potato_count` value is 4, the `elif` code block is executed, which prints `Four!`. Otherwise, the `else` code block is executed.

Twinkle, Twinkle, Little Star

Twinkle, twinkle, little star,
How I wonder what you are!
Up above the world so high,
Like a diamond in the sky.
Twinkle, twinkle, little star,
How I wonder what you are!

```python
star_size = "little"

print(f"Twinkle, twinkle, {star_size} star,")
print("How I wonder what you are!")

star_material = input("What is the star made out of? ")
print(f"The star is made out of {star_material}")

print("Up above the world so high,\nLike a diamond in the sky.")
print(f"Twinkle, twinkle, {star_size} star,")
print("How I wonder what you are!")

star_name = input("What is the name of the star? ")
print(f"The star is named {star_name.title()}")
```

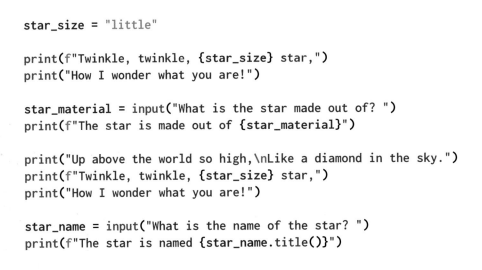

As an alternative to concatenation, strings can be formatted with **f-strings**, which are also called **formatted string literals**. An f-string begins with the letter f followed by a string that can contain variables or other expressions. Each variable or expression is enclosed in curly braces and is replaced by its value when the program runs. At the beginning of this program, the variable `star_size` is used in an f-string within `print()`, which prints `Twinkle, twinkle, little star,`. Since f-strings were introduced in Python version 3.6, they cannot be used in earlier versions of Python.

Python's built-in function `input()` reads text input from the user. The `input()` function prints the text within its parentheses (to prompt the user for text input) and pauses the program's execution to wait for the user to enter a line of text from an input device (a keyboard). After the user types a line of text and presses Enter on the keyboard, `input()` reads the text and returns it as a string. In this program, the string returned by the first `input()` is stored in the variable `star_material`, which is printed by the following `print()`.

The `input()` function is used a second time to read text input from the user, which is stored in `star_name`. The last `print()` uses the built-in method `title()`, which capitalizes the first letter of each word of the string stored in `star_name` and has empty parentheses because the method doesn't need extra information.

Here We Go Round the Mulberry Bush

1
Here we go round the mulberry bush,
The mulberry bush,
The mulberry bush.
Here we go round the mulberry bush
On a cold and frosty morning.

2
This is the way we wash our face,
Wash our face,
Wash our face.
This is the way we wash our face
On a cold and frosty morning.

3
This is the way we brush our teeth,
Brush our teeth,
Brush our teeth.
This is the way we brush our teeth
On a cold and frosty morning.

4
This is the way we comb our hair,
Comb our hair,
Comb our hair.
This is the way we comb our hair
On a cold and frosty morning

5
This is the way we put on our clothes,
Put on our clothes,
Put on our clothes.
This is the way we put on our clothes
On a cold and frosty morning.

6
Here we go round the mulberry bush,
The mulberry bush,
The mulberry bush.
Here we go round the mulberry bush
On a cold and frosty morning.

There's a lot of repetitive text in this nursery rhyme! This situation is best handled with **user-defined functions**. A user-defined function is a code block (indicated by indented lines) that performs a specific task. A **function definition** begins with the keyword def and a name. The parentheses after the function name can contain one or more **parameters** (also called **formal parameters**), which are variables that store information passed to the function. The parentheses are followed by a colon (:).

The mulberry_bush() function does not have any parameters. The how_to() function has the parameter perform_action.

You use a **function call** to execute (run) a function. The function call consists of the function's name followed by parentheses that contain values for any parameters it has. The function must be defined in the program before its function call.

```
# Function definitions

def mulberry_bush():
    print("Here we go round the mulberry bush,")
    print("The mulberry bush,")
    print("The mulberry bush.")
    print("Here we go round the mulberry bush")
    print("On a cold and frosty morning.")

def how_to(perform_action):
    print("This is the way we " + perform_action)
    print(perform_action)
    print(perform_action)
    print("This is the way we " + perform_action)
    print("On a cold and frosty morning.")

# Function calls
mulberry_bush()
how_to("wash our face")
how_to("brush our teeth")
how_to("comb our hair")
how_to("put on our clothes")
mulberry_bush()
```

The first function call executes the mulberry_bush() function, which prints the 1st verse of the nursery rhyme. Since the 6th verse has the same text as the 1st verse, the mulberry_bush() function is called again at the end of the program.

The how_to() function parameter **perform_action** receives a value (called an **argument**) that is passed to the function in its function call. The first how_to() function call prints the 2nd verse of the nursery rhyme. It passes the argument "wash our face" into the **perform_action** parameter, which is printed in the verse. The next three how_to() function calls print the 3rd to 5th verses of the nursery rhyme with different values for **perform_action**.

As you can see, a function allows a block of code to be re-used without typing it multiple times. As a result, this program is much shorter than the nursery rhyme it prints to the screen! Functions also make a program more organized and readable by breaking the program down into separate blocks of code.

I'm a Little Teapot

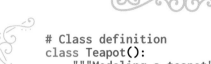

I'm a little teapot,
Short and stout,
Here is my handle
Here is my spout
When *I* get all steamed up,
Hear me shout,
Tip me over and pour me out!

```python
# Class definition
class Teapot():
    """Modeling a teapot"""

    # class attributes
    feature_1 = "handle"
    feature_2 = "spout"

    def __init__(self, height, width):
        """Initialize attributes"""
        self.height = height # Assign height parameter value to the height attribute
        self.width = width  # Assign width parameter value to the width attribute

    def tip(self):
        """Tip the teapot over"""
        print("Tip me over")

    def pour(self):
        """Pour out the teapot"""
        print("Pour me out!")

# Create an object (instance) from the Teapot class
little_teapot = Teapot("short", "stout")

print(f"I'm a little teapot, {little_teapot.height} and {little_teapot.width}")
print(f"Here is my {little_teapot.feature_1}\nHere is my {little_teapot.feature_2}")
print("When I get all steamed up,\nHear me shout,")
# Call methods on the little_teapot object
little_teapot.tip()
little_teapot.pour()
```

A **class** allows you to create an object that models something in the real world. A class contains a code block (indicated by indented lines), which provides a template (like a blueprint) for creating a specific object. **Attributes** are variables defined in the class. **Methods** are functions defined in the class. An object created from a class is called an **instance** of the class and has its own attributes and methods. Class names are capitalized by convention. The class `Teapot` models a teapot with the `tip()` and `pour()` methods and attributes of `height` and `width`. Any number of instances can be created from a class. Multiple parameters (and their corresponding arguments) in a function or method are separated by commas. `little_teapot = Teapot("short", "stout")` creates a `Teapot` instance called `little_teapot` with instance attribute values of `"short"` for `height` and `"stout"` for `width`.

Each method has a **docstring**, which acts as a comment between three single (`' '`) or three double (`"""`) quotes on each side that is often placed at the beginning of a class, function, or method to describe what it does. In a class definition, every method's first parameter must be `self`, which refers to an instance. A method call never includes an argument to the `self` parameter because Python automatically passes the instance itself as the first argument to the method. The special Python method `__init__()` (two underscores before and after init) initializes attributes. It runs automatically when an instance (object) is created.

An attribute is accessed using a dot (`.`), such as `self.height` in the class definition and `little_teapot.height` to access the `height` attribute of `little_teapot`. The methods `tip()` and `pour()` are called on the `little_teapot` instance. This prints "Tip me over" and "Pour me out!". **Class attributes** are shared by all instances of a class. Since all teapots have a handle and spout, `feature_1` and `feature_2` are defined as class attributes that store the strings `"handle"` and `"spout"`.

The Three Little Pigs

Once upon a time, three little pigs lived with their mother. One day, they left home and set out to build their own houses. Their mother told them to build sturdy houses to protect themselves against The Big Bad Wolf. The youngest pig built a house made of straw in one day. The middle pig built a house made of sticks in three days. The oldest pig built a house made of bricks in seven days.

```python
class House():
    """Modeling a house being built """

    def __init__(self, material, builder):
        """Initialize attributes"""
        self.material = material
        self.builder = builder

    def construction_time(self, time):
        """Announce how long it took to build the house"""
        print(f"The {self.builder} took {time} to build the {self.material} house.\n")

    def house_stress_test(self):
        """Test if house is still stable after the wolf tries to blow it down"""
        print("I'll huff and I'll puff and I'll blow your house down!")
        if self.material == "straw" or self.material == "wood":
            print("The " + self.material + " house is blown down!\n")
        elif self.material == "brick":
            print("You can't blow down the brick house!")
```

Continued...

In this program, the class House is used to model the construction of a house. The construction_time() method uses the **time** parameter to print the time it took to build a house with the **builder** and **material** attributes. In the house_stress_test() method, the if code block is executed if the **material** attribute value is "straw" or "wood". The elif code block is executed if the **material** attribute value is "brick".

Just as the little pigs were enjoying their new houses, The Big Bad Wolf arrived. He went to the house made of straw and shouted "Let me in little pig, or I'll huff and I'll puff and I'll blow your house down!" The wolf blew down the house made of straw. He went to the house made of sticks and shouted, "Let me in little pig, or I'll huff and I'll puff and I'll blow your house down!" The wolf blew down the house made of sticks. He went to the brick house and shouted, "Let me in little pig, or I'll huff and I'll puff and I'll blow your house down!" He tried to blow down the brick house, but it was too sturdy! The Big Bad Wolf went down the chimney of the brick house and fell right into a pot of boiling soup. He ran out of the house and never came back again. The three little pigs lived happily ever after.

```python
# Create instances of the House class
youngest_pig_home = House("straw", "youngest pig")
middle_pig_home = House("wood", "middle pig")
oldest_pig_home = House("brick", "oldest pig")

# Method calls
youngest_pig_home.construction_time("one day")
middle_pig_home.construction_time("three days")
oldest_pig_home.construction_time("seven days")
youngest_pig_home.house_stress_test()
middle_pig_home.house_stress_test()
oldest_pig_home.house_stress_test()

under_chimney = ["wood chips"]
under_chimney.insert(0,"pot of boiling soup")

if "pot of boiling soup" in under_chimney:
    print("\nThe wolf ran away after falling into the boiling soup!")
```

The youngest_pig_home instance (object) of the House class has attribute values of "straw" for material and "youngest pig" for builder. The middle_pig_home instance has attribute values of "wood" for material and "middle pig" for builder. The oldest_pig_home instance has attribute values of "brick" for material and "oldest pig" for builder. The construction_time() method is called on the three House instances, which prints the following:
The youngest pig took one day to build the straw house.
The middle pig took three days to build the wood house.
The oldest pig took seven days to build the brick house.

The first house_stress_test() method call executes the method's if code block, which prints The straw house is blown down!. The second house_stress_test() method call also executes the method's if code block, which prints The wood house is blown down!. The third house_stress_test() method call executes the method's elif code block, which prints You can't blow down the brick house!

The insert() method inserts an item into a list at a specified index. In this program, "pot of boiling soup" is inserted into the under_chimney list as the first item (index of 0).

The keyword in can be used to test if a value is contained in a sequence such as a list. The last if statement tests if "pot of boiling soup" is an item in the under_chimney list. Since this condition evaluates to be true, the if statement is executed.

Goldilocks and the Three Bears

Once upon a time, there was a girl named Goldilocks who liked to play in the woods. One day as she was chasing butterflies in the forest, she arrived at a small house. Goldilocks knocked on the door, but no one was home. She smelled delicious food, so went inside. There were three bowls of porridge on the table. She tasted the large bowl of porridge, and it was too hot. She tasted the medium-sized bowl of porridge, and it was too cold. She tasted the small bowl of porridge, and it was just right, so she ate the whole bowl!

```python
name, activity = "Goldilocks", "walking in the forest"
print(f"I'm {name} and I'm {activity}.\n")
print("I see a house!")

bears_home = False

if not bears_home:
    print("No one is home so I'll go in.\n")

large_porridge = "too hot"
medium_porridge = "too cold"
small_porridge = "just right"

if large_porridge == "too hot" or large_porridge == "too cold":
    print("The large porridge is " + large_porridge)
else:
    print("I'll eat the large porridge. It's " + large_porridge)

if medium_porridge == "too hot" or medium_porridge == "too cold":
    print("The medium-sized porridge is " + medium_porridge)
else:
    print("I'll eat the medium-sized porridge. It's " + medium_porridge)

if small_porridge == "too hot" or small_porridge == "too cold":
    print("The small porridge is " + small_porridge)
else:
    print("I'll eat the small porridge. It's " + small_porridge)
```

You can assign values to multiple variables on one line by separating the variables with commas on the left side of the equal sign and having their corresponding values separated by commas on the right side of the equal sign. "Goldilocks" is assigned to name and "walking in the forest" is assigned to activity.

The or keyword is a logical operator that tests if at least one condition is true. If the expressions to the left and right sides of the or operator are both true or if either expression is true, the overall expression is evaluated to be true. In the first if…else statement, the conditional expression tests if large_porridge stores a value of "too hot" or "too cold". Since large_porridge was assigned a value of "too hot", the if code block is executed and The large porridge is too hot is printed. Since medium_porridge was assigned a value of "too cold", the if code block of the second if…else statement is executed and The medium-sized porridge is too cold is printed. Since small_porridge was assigned a value of "just right", the else code block of the third if…else statement is executed and I'll eat the small porridge. It's just right is printed.

Goldilocks looked for a place to sit and found three chairs. She sat in the large chair and it was too hard. She sat in the medium-sized chair and it was too soft. She sat in the small chair and it was just right. However, she exceeded the chair's weight limit of 50 pounds (as shown on the label) and the chair suddenly broke into pieces!

```python
large_chair = "too hard"
medium_chair = "too soft"
small_chair = "just right"

if large_chair == "too hard" or large_chair == "too soft":
    print("The large chair is " + large_chair)
else:
    print("I'll sit in the large chair. It's " + large_chair)

if medium_chair == "too hard" or medium_chair == "too soft":
    print("The medium-sized chair is " + medium_chair)
else:
    print("I'll sit in the medium-sized chair. It's " + medium_chair)

if small_chair == "too hard" or small_chair == "too soft":
    print("The small chair is " + small_chair)
else:
    print("I'll sit in the small chair. It's " + small_chair)
    weight = 60
    if (weight >= 51):
        print("The chair is breaking!")
    else:
        print("This is a sturdy chair.")
```

This program's three if...else statements are structured in the same way as in the last program. The values of large_chair, medium_chair, and small_chair are tested for being equal to "too hard" or "too soft". The if code block of the first if...else statement is executed, which prints The large chair is too hard. The if code block of the second if...else statement is executed, which prints The medium-sized chair is too soft.

The else code block of the third if...else statement is executed, which contains an inner (nested) if...else statement. The inner if statement tests if weight is greater than or equal to 51 using the **greater than or equal to** comparison operator (>=), which returns True if the left-hand operand is greater than or equal to the right-hand operand. Since weight has a value of 60, the inner if statement is executed and The chair is breaking! is printed.

WEIGHT LIMIT:
50 LBS

Goldilocks was looking for a place to rest and found three beds. She climbed into the large bed and it was too hard. She climbed into the medium-sized bed and it was too soft. She climbed into the small bed, and it was just right, so she fell asleep. The three bears who lived in the house returned from their walk and found Goldilocks asleep in the small bed. They woke her up and she ran out the door!

```python
import time

large_bed = "too hard"
medium_bed = "too soft"
small_bed = "just right"

if large_bed == "too hard" or large_bed == "too soft":
    print("The large bed is " + large_bed)
else:
    print("I'll sleep in the large bed. It's " + large_bed)

if medium_bed == "too hard" or medium_bed == "too soft":
    print("The medium-sized bed is " + medium_bed)
else:
    print("I'll sleep in the medium-sized bed. It's " + medium_bed)

if small_bed == "too hard" or small_bed == "too soft":
    print("The small bed is " + small_bed)
else:
    print("I'll sleep in the small bed. It's " + small_bed)

time.sleep(5)

bears_home = True

if bears_home:
    print("\nRun!")
```

A **module** is a file that can contain Python definitions (such as functions, classes, or variables) and statements. A module allows you to organize related code in a separate file from your main program file and easily use the code in different programs. `time` is one of Python's built-in modules that is part of the **Python Standard Library**, which contains a collection of modules that are useful for performing common tasks. The `import` keyword is used to import a module into your program so you can use its code. To call a function from the module that was imported, place a dot (.) between the module name and function name. The `time` module contains the `sleep()` function, which suspends program execution for the number of seconds specified by the argument in parentheses. When `time.sleep(5)` is executed, the next line of code is executed five seconds later.

This program's three if…else statements are structured in the same way as in the previous two programs. The if…else statements print:
```
The large bed is too hard
The medium-sized bed is too soft
I'll sleep in the small bed. It's just right
```

Jack and the Beanstalk

Once upon a time, a boy named Jack lived in a cottage with his mother. One day, she told him to go to the town and trade their cow for money. In the town, Jack was convinced by a strange man to trade his cow for magic beans. When he got back home, his mother was angry and threw the magic beans out the window. The next morning, Jack saw a huge beanstalk growing outside! He decided to climb it.

```python
# Function definitions

def trade(valuable_item):
    if valuable_item == "cow":
        return "magic beans"
    return "money"

def throw_from_window(item):
    print("Why did you throw the " + item + " out the window?")
    if item == "magic beans":
        return "giant beanstalk"
    return item

def climb_to_castle(visit_number):
    items_in_castle = ["a bag of gold coins", "a hen", "a magical harp"]
    if visit_number == 1:
        print("I'm climbing to the castle for the first time")
        item_taken = items_in_castle.pop(0)
    elif visit_number == 2:
        print("I'm climbing to the castle for the second time")
        item_taken = items_in_castle.pop(1)
    elif visit_number == 3:
        print("I'm climbing to the castle for the third time")
        item_taken = items_in_castle.pop(2)
        print("The giant chased after me and I cut the beanstalk down!")
    else:
        item_taken = ""
    if item_taken:
        print("I brought back " + item_taken)
        return item_taken
```

Continued...

The `return` keyword is used to exit a function and return a value to the function call line. In the `trade()` and `throw_from_window()` functions, an `if` statement is used to execute a different `return` statement based on the function's parameter value. In the `climb_to_castle()` function, the last `if` statement is executed if `item_taken` is a non-empty string. An empty string (`""`) evaluates to `False`.

Jack climbed up the beanstalk to a castle at the top, where a giant was sleeping. Jack took a bag of gold coins and climbed down the beanstalk before the giant woke up. Jack climbed the beanstalk again and took back a hen that laid golden eggs. After Jack climbed to the castle for the third time, he took a magical harp. The giant heard the harp play as Jack was leaving and he chased him down the beanstalk. Jack rushed down fast enough to cut the beanstalk before the giant could catch him. Jack and his mother lived happily ever after.

```
my_item = "cow"

returned_item = trade(my_item)
print("I got " + returned_item + " in return for my " + my_item)

if returned_item != "money":
    item_outside = throw_from_window(returned_item)
    if item_outside == "giant beanstalk":
        print("There's a giant beanstalk outside now!")
        new_item_1 = climb_to_castle(visit_number = 1)
        new_item_2 = climb_to_castle(visit_number = 2)
        new_item_3 = climb_to_castle(visit_number = 3)

        all_items = [new_item_1, new_item_2, new_item_3]

        print("I now have these items:")
        for item in all_items:
            print(item)
        print("Now we can live happily ever after.")
```

my_item is the argument passed to the trade() function's valuable_item parameter. Since my_item has a value of "cow", the statement return "magic beans" is executed. This return statement causes the function to exit, so the statement return "money" is not reached. The return value of "magic beans" is stored in returned_item.

The **not equal operator** (!=) compares two values and returns True if they are not equal. If the left-hand operand equals the right-hand operand, it returns False. The expression returned_item != "money" evaluates to True because returned_item holds the value of "magic beans". Therefore, the if statement is executed. The inner (nested) if statement is also executed because item_outside has a value of "giant beanstalk" that was returned from throw_from_window().

Each climb_to_castle() function call uses a **keyword argument**, which directly matches the function's parameter name with the argument value. On the other hand, **positional arguments** don't use parameter names in a function call, as seen in the trade() and throw_from_window() function calls. If multiple positional arguments (separated by commas) are used, they are listed in the same order as their corresponding parameters.

Since visit_number has a value of 1 in the first climb_to_castle() function call, the first if code block of climb_to_castle() is executed and pop() removes the first item of items_in_castle, which is "a bag of gold coins". This value is stored in item_taken, which is returned from the function and stored in new_item_1. The next two climb_to_castle() function calls return "a hen" and "a magical harp" from the function. The list all_items is created, which contains the variables storing the three climb_to_castle() return values. Each list item is printed in a for loop.

Little Red Riding Hood

Once upon a time, there was a girl known as Little Red Riding Hood. One day, her mother asked her to bring a basket of food (cupcakes, cookies, and donuts) to her grandmother because she wasn't feeling well. As Little Red Riding Hood was walking through the forest to her grandmother's house, a wolf asked her where she was going. Little Red Riding Hood told the wolf she was going to granny's house.

```python
# Function definitions

def into_the_woods(basket_items):
    print("I'm going to granny's house with these items:")
    for item in basket_items:
        print(item)

def scare_wolf(object, person = "a hunter"):
    print(f"I'm {person}. I'll scare the wolf away with {object}!\n")
    print("The wolf is gone!\n")
    return "Granny"

items_to_bring = ("cupcakes", "cookies", "donuts")

into_the_woods(items_to_bring)  # Function call

print("\nHi Granny!")
features_seen = {"ears": "big", "eyes": "big", "hands": "big", "teeth": "big"}
```

Continued...

items_to_bring is a **tuple**, which is a Python data type that contains a collection of items within parentheses. A tuple is a sequence of items like a list, but the items cannot be changed. Since you cannot add or remove items from a tuple, use it when you have a collection of items that don't need to be updated. items_to_bring is the argument passed to the into_the_woods() function, in which each item of the tuple stored in basket_items is printed in the for loop

Once she arrived at the house, she thought her grandmother looked peculiar. She exclaimed, "My, what big ears you have!", "My, what big eyes you have!", "My, what big hands you have!", and "My, what big teeth you have!". Little Red Riding Hood then realized a wolf was in granny's clothing and she screamed. A hunter heard her and ran into the house. He scared off the wolf with his axe and recovered Little Red Riding Hood's grandmother.

```python
big_counter = 0
for feature, size in features_seen.items():
    if size == "big":
        print("My, what big " + feature + " you have!")
        big_counter += 1     # this is the same as big_counter = big_counter + 1

    # test if the counter value equals the number of dictionary items
    if big_counter == len(features_seen):
        wolf = True
    else:
        wolf = False

    if wolf:
        shout = "ahhh"
        print(shout.upper() + " it's a wolf!")

person_rescued = scare_wolf("my axe")
print(person_rescued + " and Little Red Riding Hood are safe!")
```

The key:value pairs of the features_seen dictionary are iterated over in a for loop. If the dictionary value stored in size for the current iteration has a value of "big", the value of big_counter is incremented by 1 with the **addition assignment operator** (+=). The value on the right side of the addition assignment operator is added to the variable's value.

After the for loop ends, an if statement tests if the value of big_counter is equal to the length of the dictionary. The len() function returns the length (number of items) of the features_seen dictionary. The if condition is true, so wolf is assigned the value of True and the next if statement is executed. Python's upper() method converts all lowercase characters of a string into uppercase characters and returns the uppercase string. AHHH it's a wolf! is printed.

The scare_wolf() function's parameter person has a **default value** of "a hunter". If you don't want to use the default value, an argument can be specified in the function call. In a function definition, parameters with default values must be placed after all the parameters without default values. The argument "my axe" matches up with the first parameter object. The function parameters are used to print I'm a hunter. I'll scare the wolf away with my axe!. The return value "Granny" is stored in person_rescued, which is then printed in a sentence.

The Princess and the Pea

Once upon a time, there was a prince who couldn't find a princess to marry. One stormy night, a girl arrived at the castle and said she was a princess. The king and queen let her into the castle to stay for the night in the guest room. The queen wanted to test if she was really a princess, so she put a pea on top of the bed's mattress and then stacked 20 mattresses on top of it. She then stacked 20 feather beds on top of that. "Sweet dreams!" said the queen.

```python
print("Knock Knock\nWho's there?\nA princess\nA princess…who? We'll see about that…")
princess = None

bed = ["original mattress"]
bed.append("pea")

for mattress in range(1,21):
    bed.append("new mattress #" + str(mattress))

for feather_bed in range(1,21):
    bed.append("feather bed #" + str(feather_bed))

print("You are now going to sleep on a bed stacked with these items:\n")
for bed_item in bed:
    print(bed_item)

print("\nSweet dreams!\n")
```

Continued...

Python's append() method adds an item to the end of a list. The first append() method call acts on the bed list to add "pea" to the end of the list. The range() function generates a sequence of integer numbers and is used to repeat the for loop for a specified number of times. In this program, the range start value is 1 and the stop value is 21, which generates integer values from 1 through 20 because the stop value is not included. For each iteration of the first for loop, the current number generated by range() is stored in the variable mattress. The for loop repeats for each integer value from 1 through 20.

The first for loop appends "new mattress #1" through "new mattress #20" to the end of the bed list. The second for loop appends "feather bed #1" through "feather bed #20" to the end of the bed list. Each item of the bed list is printed in the third for loop.

The queen decided that if the girl felt the pea under all the mattresses and feather beds, she must be a princess. After the girl woke up, the queen asked her how well she slept. The girl responded that she didn't sleep well at all because she felt a lump under the bed. The queen exclaimed, "You must be a princess!" and proceeded to put the pea into a glass case. The prince and (now) princess fell in love and got married. They lived happily ever after.

```python
print("How well did you sleep on a scale of 0-10?")
sleep_quality = 0
print(sleep_quality)

if sleep_quality < 3:
    princess = True

if princess:
    print("Oh, you must be a princess!")
    pea = bed.pop(1)
    print("We'll put the " + pea + " into a glass case.")
    print("Now we'll have to figure out where to put these items:")
    for item in bed[1:]:
        print(item)
```

The **less than operator** (<) is a comparison (relational) operator that returns True if the value on the left side of the operator is less than the value on the right side of the operator. Since sleep_quality has a value of 0, the first if statement is executed and princess is assigned the value of True. In the next if statement, the second item (index of 1) of the bed list is removed by pop() and the value ("pea") is stored in pea.

The nested for loop iterates over a slice of the bed list. The slice bed[1:] includes the second item at an index of 1 and ends through the last item because the ending index is omitted. Therefore, the only bed item that is not printed is the first item ("original mattress").

The Gingerbread Man

Once upon a time, an old woman and an old man lived in a cottage in the countryside. The old woman decided to make gingerbread cookies for dessert.

```python
from math import ceil as round_up

gingerbread_recipe = {
    "flour": [3, "cups"],
    "eggs": [2, "whole"],
    "unsalted butter": [3/4, "cup"],
    "baking soda": [3/4, "teaspoon"],
    "ground ginger": [3/4, "tablespoon"],
    "ground cinnamon": [1, "tablespoon"],
    "ground cloves": [1/2, "teaspoon"],
    "ground nutmeg": [1/2, "teaspoon"],
    "salt": [1/2, "teaspoon"],
    "ground black pepper": [1/4, "teaspoon"],
    "dark brown sugar": [1/2, "cup"],
    }

# This recipe makes 20 gingerbread cookies. Enter a numerical value.
cookie_num = int(input("How many gingerbread cookies do you want to make? "))

batches = round_up(cookie_num / 20)  # round up to next batch number (for fractional value)
print(f"A batch quantity of {batches} is needed to make {cookie_num} cookies.")
print("The gingerbread cookie recipe calls for:")
for ingredient, amount in gingerbread_recipe.items():
    print(f"{amount[0] * batches} {amount[1]} {ingredient}")
```

Continued...

math is one of Python's built-in modules in the Python Standard Library containing functions that perform mathematical calculations. A specific function or class (or other definition such as a list) can be imported from a module without importing the entire module using the from keyword. This allows the imported function or class to be called by name in the program (without using the module name and dot). The imported function or class can be given a different name in the program with the keyword as. In this program, the ceil() function is imported from the math module and ceil is renamed to round_up.

Python's built-in int() function can be used to convert a numerical string's data type into an integer data type. Since the input() function always returns a string, int() is used to convert the string returned from input() into an integer, which is stored in cookie_num. Math cannot be performed with a string, so this allows the value to be used as a number. The math module's ceil() function rounds a floating-point value (a number with a decimal point) up to the nearest integer. cookie_num / 20 divides cookie_num by 20 with the division operator (/), which always returns a floating-point value. The number of cookie batches needed is calculated from ceil() (renamed to round_up) given the argument of cookie_num / 20 because there are 20 cookies in a batch.

The gingerbread_recipe dictionary has a list for the value of each key:value pair. The first item of each list represents the quantity of the ingredient (the key) and the second item represents the measurement unit. In the for loop, amount[0] is the first item of the list in the current loop iteration and amount[1] is the second item of the list. amount[0] is multiplied by batches with the **multiplication operator** (*) to display the appropriate amount of each ingredient for the batch quantity.

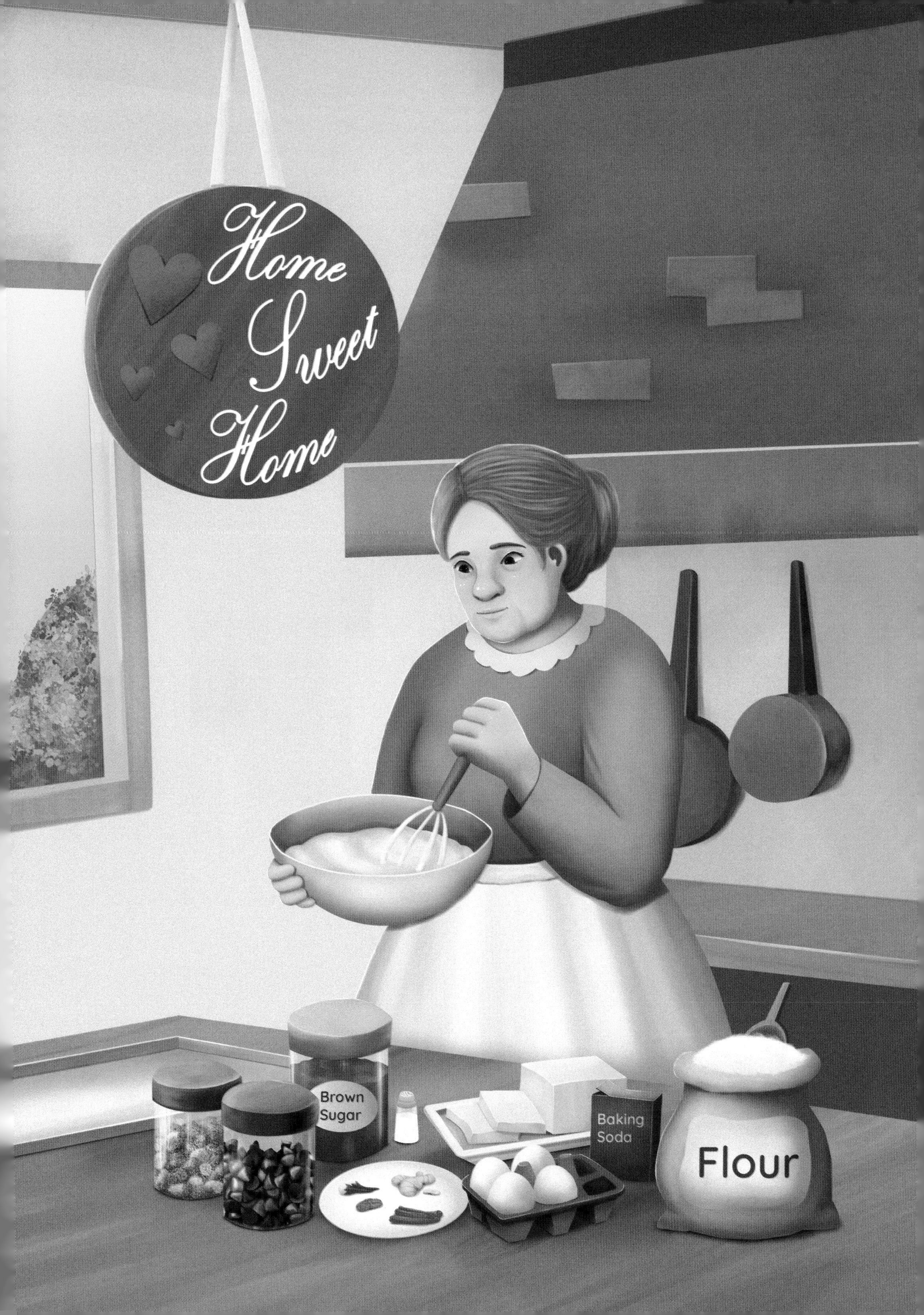
Home
Sweet
Home
Brown
Sugar
Baking
Soda
Flour

First, the old woman decided to make a unique gingerbread cookie in the shape of a man. She followed the gingerbread cookie recipe and mixed the ingredients. Next, she added two gumdrops for the gingerbread man's buttons, two chocolate chips for his eyes, and frosting for his mouth. She baked the cookie at 350 °F for ten minutes. She opened the oven and much to her astonishment, the gingerbread man ran out! She chased after him. He shouted, "Run, run as fast as you can, you can't catch me, I'm The Gingerbread Man!" Next, the gingerbread man ran past the old man in the garden and shouted, "I've already run away from an old woman, and I can run away from you!" The old man ran and the gingerbread man shouted, "Run, run as fast as you can, you can't catch me, I'm The Gingerbread Man!"

```python
chase_list = [] # Create empty list

# Function definitions

def bake_cookie(bake_temp, minutes):
    print("\nI set the oven temperature to " + bake_temp)
    while minutes > 0:
        print("Timer: " + str(minutes) + " minutes")
        minutes = minutes - 1
    return "gingerbread man"

def prep_cookie(shape, *decorations):
    print("\nI mixed the ingredients and shaped the cookie dough into a " + shape)
    print("I'm adding these decorations:")
    for decoration in decorations:
        print(decoration)

def new_chase(new_chaser, chased):
    print(f"\nI'm {new_chaser}, stop running!\n")
    global chase_list
    if chase_list:
        print("I have run away from")
        for chaser in chase_list:
            print(chaser)
        print("and I can run away from you!")
    chase_list.append(new_chaser)
    print("Run, run, as fast as you can, you can't catch me, I'm " + chased)
```

In the bake_cookie() function, there is a while loop. A while loop executes its code block if the condition after while is true. The loop repeats if its condition is still true after it executes and it continues to repeat until the condition is false. During each loop iteration, minutes is decremented by 1 with the **subtraction operator** (-). The while condition tests if minutes is greater than 0 with the **greater than** (>) operator. Once minutes has a value of 0, the while condition is false and the loop does not repeat again. The function exits with a return value of "gingerbread man". In prep_cookie(), the asterisk (*) before the decorations parameter makes it an empty tuple that accepts any number of arguments, which are called **arbitrary arguments.**

A variable defined within a function is called a **local variable** and is only available to that function. A variable defined outside of a function is called a **global variable** and can be used anywhere in the program. Although a function can access a global variable's value, it can't modify the value unless the variable is declared to be global with the global keyword in the function. chase_list, a global variable that is assigned an empty list, is declared with global so that items can be added to it in the new_chase() function. append() acts on chase_list to add the value of the new_chaser parameter to the end of the list.

Next, the gingerbread man met a pig. He shouted, "I've already run away from an old woman, an old man, and I can run away from you!" The pig ran and the gingerbread man shouted, "Run, run as fast as you can, you can't catch me, I'm The Gingerbread Man!" Next, the gingerbread man met a cow. He shouted, "I've already run away from an old woman, an old man, a pig, and I can run away from you!" The cow ran and he shouted, "Run, run as fast as you can, you can't catch me, I'm The Gingerbread Man!" Next, the gingerbread man met a horse. He shouted, "I've already run away from an old woman, an old man, a pig, a cow, and I can run away from you!" The horse ran and he shouted, "Run, run as fast as you can, you can't catch me, I'm The Gingerbread Man!" The gingerbread man was eventually blocked by a river and met a fox that offered to take him across it. The gingerbread man hopped on his back, but once the fox asked him to hop on his nose, the gingerbread man became nervous and was able to hop onto the other side of the river instead. The gingerbread man escaped and ran away.

```python
print("\nFirst, I will make a gingerbread cookie that looks like a person.\n")
prep_cookie("man", "two gumdrops", "two chocolate chips", "frosting")
special_cookie = bake_cookie("350 F", 10)
print("\nThe " + special_cookie + " is done! I'll take it out of the oven.")
cookie_name = "The " + special_cookie.title()
print(cookie_name + " is running away!")

obstacle = None
while not obstacle:
    new_chase("an old woman", cookie_name)
    new_chase("an old man", cookie_name)
    new_chase("a pig", cookie_name)
    new_chase("a cow", cookie_name)
    new_chase("a horse", cookie_name)
    obstacle = "river"

print("\nI'm a fox, hop on my back and I'll take you across the " + obstacle)
chase_list.clear() # clear the list
print("\nNow hop on my nose.\nI will hop away instead.")
new_chase("a fox", cookie_name)
```

In the `prep_cookie()` function call, `"man"` is passed to the **shape** parameter. The arguments `"two gumdrops"`, `"two chocolate chips"`, and `"frosting"` are passed to the **decorations** parameter, which is a tuple due to the asterisk (`*`) before it. The `bake_cookie()` function call passes `"350 F"` to the **bake_temp** parameter and passes 10 to the **minutes** parameter. The `bake_cookie()` function returns `"gingerbread man"`, which is stored in **special_cookie**. The `title()` method acts on **special_cookie**, thereby making **cookie_name** store `"The Gingerbread Man"`.

obstacle is assigned `None`, which evaluates to `False`. Therefore, the `while` loop's condition `not obstacle` evaluates to `True` since the `not` keyword inverts the Boolean value of `False`. In the `new_chase()` function, the `if` statement executes if **chase_list** is a non-empty list, which evaluates to `True`. This occurs for the 2nd to 5th `new_chase()` function calls. The items of the list are printed in the `if` code block. After the five `new_chase()` function calls, **obstacle** is assigned a value of `"river"`. The `while` loop exits because **obstacle** is now a non-empty string that evaluates to `True`, thereby making the condition `not obstacle` evaluate to `False`. The `clear()` method removes all items of a list. After **chase_list** is cleared, there is another `new_chase()` function call. Since **chase_list** is now an empty list, the `if` statement in `new_chase()` is not executed. The value of `"a fox"` is added to **chase_list**.

Cinderella

Once upon a time, a girl named Cinderella lived with her evil stepmother and two evil stepsisters. They made her do all their chores. One day, a messenger arrived at the house with an invitation to meet Prince Charming at the royal ball. On the day of the ball, Cinderella was told she couldn't attend because she had too many chores to do. She was very upset, but suddenly out of nowhere her fairy godmother appeared and said she would help her get to the ball. The fairy godmother transformed a pumpkin into a carriage, mice into horses, a rat into a coachman, and Cinderella's old dress into a new gown. She also gave Cinderella two glass slippers. The fairy godmother told Cinderella the spell would wear off at midnight, at which time the transformed things would go back to their original states.

```python
from datetime import date
print("Today, " + str(date.today()) +  ", is the ball!\n")

done_with_chores = False

if not done_with_chores:
    print("I can't go to the ball.\n")

print("I am your fairy godmother and I will make all your dreams come true.")

magic_transformation = {
    "pumpkin": "a carriage",
    "mice": "horses",
    "rat": "a coachman",
    "old dress": "a new gown"
    }

for thing, transformed_thing in magic_transformation.items():
    print("The " + thing + " transformed into " + transformed_thing)

new_shoes = "glass slippers"
print("Oh, and I also got you " + new_shoes)
glass_slippers_total = 2
print("The magic spell wears off at midnight. Have fun!\n")
```

Continued...

The `date` class is imported from the `datetime` module. The `today()` method in the `date` class returns the current local date (year, month, and day). In the first `print()`, `date.today()` is converted into a string because it returns a `datetime.date` object rather than a value with a string data type. Each key:value pair of the `magic_transformation` dictionary is printed in a sentence in the `for` loop.

Cinderella arrived at the hall at 8 o'clock. She danced with Prince Charming until she realized the clock was striking midnight and she promptly ran away. As she was running down the palace stairs, one of her glass slippers fell off and she didn't even notice. She rode back home in the carriage, which soon turned back into a pumpkin. The horses turned back into mice, the coachman turned back into a rat, and her new gown turned back into her old dress. She walked the rest of the way home.

```python
hour = 8

while hour <= 11:
    print("I'm dancing with Prince Charming!\n")
    hour += 1    # This is the same as hour = hour + 1
    print("The clock just struck " + str(hour))

print("Oh no, it's midnight! Bye Prince Charming, I have to run!\n")

# This is the same as glass_slippers_total = glass_slippers_total - 1
glass_slippers_total -= 1

if glass_slippers_total % 2:
    print("Cinderella lost a glass slipper!\n")

print("The magic spell is over. The following things are back:")
for thing in magic_transformation.keys():
    print(thing)
```

Continued...

The **less than or equal to operator** (<=) in the while condition returns True if the left-hand operand is less than or equal to the right-hand operand. Since hour was assigned a value of 8, the while loop is executed and repeats three times. Once hour is incremented to 12, the while loop's condition is false and the loop doesn't repeat again.

The **subtraction assignment operator** (-=) is used to decrement the value of glass_slippers_total by 1, so it now has a value of 1. The **modulo operator** (%) returns the remainder after its left-hand operand is divided by its right-hand operand. The expression glass_slippers_total % 2 returns 1 because the remainder of 1 divided by 2 is 1. A non-zero value is evaluated to be true and a value of zero is evaluated to be false. Therefore, the if statement is executed.

The built-in keys() method returns a list of a dictionary's keys. In this program, it's used in the for loop to iterate over only the keys of the magic_transformation dictionary. The keys pumpkin, mice, rat, and old dress are printed in the for loop.

Prince Charming found Cinderella's missing glass slipper on the stairs and was determined to find the girl it belonged to. He decided to ask every girl in the land to try on the slipper to see if it was a perfect fit. When he went to Cinderella's house, her two stepsisters ran to the door and tried on the glass slipper. It did not fit either of them. Prince Charming noticed Cinderella cleaning upstairs and asked her to try on the glass slipper. It was a perfect fit! Cinderella and Prince Charming got married and lived happily ever after at the palace.

```python
# Function definition
def glass_slipper_fit_test(person):
    slipper_fit = "perfect fit" if person == "Cinderella" else "bad fit"
    print("The glass slipper is a " + slipper_fit)
    global found_girl
    found_girl = True if slipper_fit == "perfect fit" else False
    if found_girl:
        print("Therefore, " + person + " must be the girl I met at the ball!\n")
    else:
        print("Therefore, " + person + " is not the girl I met at the ball\n")

print("\nI need to find the girl this glass slipper belongs to!\n")
glass_slipper_fit_test("the first stepsister")
glass_slipper_fit_test("the second stepsister")

print("Prince Charming asked Cinderella to try on the glass slipper.\n")
glass_slipper_fit_test("Cinderella")
if found_girl:
    glass_slippers_total += 1
    print("Cinderella now has " + str(glass_slippers_total) + " glass slippers")
    print("Cinderella and Prince Charming lived happily ever after.")
```

In the `glass_slipper_fit_test()` function, `"perfect fit" if person == "Cinderella" else "bad fit"` is a type of conditional expression known as a **ternary operator**. On a single line, it returns one of two values based on a condition being true or false. This is a shorter alternative to using an if...else statement. First, the condition after `if` is evaluated, which is `person == "Cinderella"`. If the condition is true, the value before `if` is returned, which is `"perfect fit"`. If the condition is false, the value after `else` is returned, which is `"bad fit"`. The returned value is stored in `slipper_fit`.

`found_girl` is declared with the `global` keyword, which makes it a global variable that can be used outside the scope of the function. There is a second ternary operator that returns `True` if `slipper_fit` has a value of `"perfect fit"` and otherwise returns `False`. The returned value is stored in `found_girl`.

The first `glass_slipper_fit_test()` function call prints `The glass slipper is a bad fit` and `Therefore, the first stepsister is not the girl I met at the ball`. The second `glass_slipper_fit_test()` function call prints `The glass slipper is a bad fit` and `Therefore, the second stepsister is not the girl I met at the ball`. The third `glass_slipper_fit_test()` function call prints `The glass slipper is a perfect fit` and `Therefore, Cinderella must be the girl I met at the ball!`

Since the `found_girl` value was set to `True` in the function, the last `if` statement is executed. The value of `glass_slippers_total` is incremented by 1 and then printed in the sentence `Cinderella now has 2 glass slippers`.

Run the Programs!

Now you can share the nursery rhymes and fairy tales with YOUR computer! A **Python interpreter** is a program that executes the instructions from a Python program's **source code** (the code you wrote in your program). A Python **IDE** (integrated development environment) contains an editor in which you write code and a Python interpreter that executes the code. To write and run programs, you can download and install a Python IDE or use an online Python interpreter.

Download Python

There are many IDEs you can use to write and run Python programs. **IDLE** is the IDE that is included with the download of Python from the official Python website's download page:

https://www.python.org/downloads/

1. Click the Download button at the top of the page to download the latest Python version for Windows.
2. Once the download finishes, click on it. If you're prompted to run the file, click Run.
3. In the next window, check the box for "**Add Python** [*version #*] **to PATH**". The box for **Install launcher for all users (recommended)** should be checked. Next, click "**Install Now**".
4. Once the installation is complete, open IDLE by clicking on IDLE within the Python folder in the start menu or searching for IDLE on the start menu's search bar and opening the app.

If you're using a Mac, click the link to download Python for Mac and click the latest release at the top of the page. Click on the Mac OS installer for your computer below the Files section at the bottom of the page. Click on the download once it is complete and follow the prompts to install Python.

Writing and running a Python script

When you first open IDLE, you'll see the **Python IDLE shell**, which can run one line of code at a time. You can type a line of code after the >>> prompt and press *Enter* on the keyboard to see the result printed from the interpreter. However, since you want to run multi-line programs (and be able to save your work!), follow these steps to create and run a **Python script**, which is a file that contains your Python program.

1. Click File -> New File, which opens a text editor window. Enter the program code.
3. Click File -> Save. Enter a filename (which has the extension **.py**). Click Save.
4. Click Run -> Run Module to run the script.
5. You'll see the output from your program's print() function(s) in the Python IDLE shell!

Congratulations

You are now a Python programmer!

Change the Stories

Change the values of variables and see how the output changes. What if Jack didn't fall down the hill?

Common Errors

Code editors highlight different types of code with different colors, which is called syntax highlighting. For example, comments are all highlighted with the same color. This makes the code easier to read.

If you get an error after running the code, fix the code and run it again! There are many common syntax errors. Make sure to:

- Include a colon (`:`) at the end of the line after `def`, `class`, `for`, `while`, `if`, `else`, or `elif`
- Indent all lines in a code block by the same number of spaces. You can't mix tabs and spaces.
- Insert the correct number of quotation marks and parentheses and place them correctly. You'll also get an error if you copy and paste quotes (such as from a word processor) written in unicode format ("Hi!") rather than ASCII format (`"Hi!"`). When you type quotation marks directly into the code editor, it will be in ASCII format.
- Write Python keywords with the correct spelling and capitalization. All keywords are lowercase except `True`, `False`, and `None`.

You Don't Need a Magic Wand

Now you can make things move by programming them! Python is often used in robotics for processing sensor data and controlling robots (such as the movement of robot arms) with high-level commands. Python can also be used for a wide variety of software applications including data science and analysis, artificial intelligence (AI) and machine learning, scientific and numeric computing, web development and apps, and game development.

Physical Computing

You can use Python in physical computing, which involves programming a computer to sense and interact with the outside world. For example, an external computer can control a robot or the computer can be embedded within the robot. Python is used to provide high-level instructions for reading sensor inputs (such as from a light or temperature sensor) and controlling outputs (such as a motor or LED).

A microcontroller has all the components of a computer contained in a single chip and is designed to be embedded within a larger device or appliance. The micro:bit (**https://microbit.org**) is a microcontroller development board designed for beginners that is commonly programmed in Python. The Raspberry Pi® (**https://www.raspberrypi.org**) is a single-board computer commonly programmed in Python. Unlike a microcontroller, the Raspberry Pi board is a higher power general-purpose computer that runs an operating system. It can be easily connected to the internet and used as a desktop computer by connecting it to a monitor, mouse, and keyboard. You can also connect electronic components to the Raspberry Pi to read sensor inputs and control outputs with Python code.

Raspberry Pi is a trademark of the Raspberry Pi Foundation

Notes

Notes

Notes

Notes

Also by Shari Eskenas

A Day in Code
An illustrated story written in
the C programming language
ISBN: 978-1-73590-791-8 (paperback)
978-1-73590-790-1 (hardcover)

A Day in Code- Python
Learn to code in Python
through an illustrated story
ISBN: 978-1-73590-794-9 (paperback)
978-1-73590-793-2 (hardcover)

You're Invited

Join the celebration at
www.sundaelectronics.com/fairytales